The
Birth of the Ganga

Other works by Harish Johari

The
Birth of the Ganga

Harish Johari

Illustrated by
Harish Johari and Pieter Weltevrede

INNER
TRADITIONS
INDIA

Inner Traditions India

In the United States:
One Park Street
Rochester, Vermont 05767
USA

In India:
1007/1008 Arcadia
195 Nariman Point
Mumbai 400 021, India

www.InnerTraditions.com

Inner Traditions India is a division of Inner Traditions International

LIBRARY OF CONGRESS CATALOGING-IN PUBLICATION DATA
Johari, Harish, 1934–
The birth of the Ganga / Harish Johari ; illustrated by Harish Johari
and Pieter Weltevrede
p. cm.
ISBN 0-89281-690-2 (alk. paper)
1. Gaṅgā (Hindu deity). 2. Mythology, Hindu. I. Title.
BL1225.G35J65 1998   98-15300
294.5'211— dc21 CIP

Printed and bound in the United States

10   9   8   7   6   5   4   3   2   1

Text design by Tim Jones and Peri Champine
This book was typeset in Times New Roman with Fine Hand, Zither, Black
Chancery, and Barbara Svelte as the display typefaces

Aum Shri Ganeshaye Namah Aum

Introduction

Consciousness, when manifested, goes through a cycle of creation, preservation, and destruction. These three functions are attributed to three divinities: creation to Brahma, preservation to Vishnu, and destruction to Shiva. These three divinities form the trinity of the Hindu pantheon.

The stream of consciousness of Ganga comes from the combined energy of Brahma, Vishnu, and Shiva. The energy originates from the big toe of Vishnu and then is collected by Brahma and given a charming divine form. Ganga's birth in Brahma Loka makes all the high beings who live in the higher lokas happy. Then she is cursed by Rishi Durvasa for her impertinence and is forced to descend from the higher lokas to Earth as a river. The moment of her descent from Heaven to Earth comes when the human Bhagirath, through his diligent worship of Brahma, is able to get Brahma to release Ganga in order to purify and liberate the souls of his cursed ancestors at the ashram of Sage Kapil.

Before Ganga descends to Earth, she is held captive in the hairlocks of Shiva and becomes charged with the energy of Shiva. She already contains the combined energy of Bhrama and Vishnu and now she is charged by the energy of all three divinities—Brahma, Vishnu, and Shiva. In her journey to

Sage Kapil's ashram, where she meets the ocean (Sagar), she is swallowed by Rishi Janu and becomes additionally charged with Janu's holy energy. She is now even purer than before and is able to purify anyone who comes in contact with her holy water.

The special feature of Ganga's holiness is constantly displayed by her water, which does not decay if stored in any container. Navigators who traveled by ship from Calcutta to London testified that the Ganga water they carried in their ships did not spoil during their journey, but when they returned from London to Calcutta without Ganga water, they had to stop frequently for fresh water at many places because the water would spoil in taste and odor within a week.

Ganga water is still kept in every Hindu household and all Hindus aspire to get a drop or two of this holy water at the moment of their death to purify their soul and take them to the higher lokas. The Ayurvedic scriptures of Charak Samhita and Vagbhatta also praise the medicinal qualities of Ganga water. Muslim King Aurangzeb, who was opposed to everything that was not Islamic, drank only Ganga water because of its healing properties. And Akbar the Great and many other Muslim kings sent camel caravans to bring water from the river Ganga for their personal use.

Ganga herself is not only purifying, but the environment in which she flows gets charged by spiritual energy that inspires sages and common people equally. Most of the valuable Hindu scriptures were written by sages who lived on the banks of the river.

Although Ganga's water is healing and holy, she is not only a river. Divine energy Ganga as a woman marries and begets children. She is the biological mother of Bhishma, the grandsire and hero of the great epic Mahabharata.

Ganga's story is as purifying as is her water and reading or listening to her story awakens the spiritual side of our existence. It is said that in the Kali Yuga the only source of purification is Ganga.

The story of Ganga exists in many Hindu texts. The story that appears in this book is taken principally from the Skanda Puranam, the Mahabharata, and the Brahannaradiye Puranam.

The
Birth of the Ganga

*I*n a time long gone by, there was born a very powerful demon known by the name of Bali, from the family of Prahlad and Virochana, the demons of ancient India.

By performing rigorous austerities, by charity, and by following hard disciplines, Bali acquired so much power that he became invincible. He conquered the three worlds of Swarga Loka (Heaven), Bhu Loka (Earth), and Patal Loka (the Underworld); drove the gods out of their abode in Swarga Loka; and became the unchallenged king of all three worlds.

*B*ali prohibited the worship of gods in the three lokas. When the dwellers of Bhu Loka stopped performing the homa (fire sacrifice) and stopped making offerings to the gods, the gods began to starve because they drew their life force from the offerings made by the dwellers of Earth.

The defeated gods assembled and went to Lord Brahma, creator of the world.

"Save us, Grandsire," they pleaded. "Save us from the tyranny of Bali. We have been excommunicated from our abode in Swarga Loka and are forced to hide from Bali's soldiers as mere mortals on Earth. Please bring peace and happiness again to Earth and Heaven."

Lord Brahma consoled the gods, saying, "You have brought this disaster upon yourselves by indulging in enjoyment and amusement. You became proud of your powers and moved away from the path of discipline.

"King Bali, on the contrary, is constantly involved in doing acts of virtue. He is disciplined and has taken a vow of charity. His doors are always open for the needy and poor and everyone gets whatever he or she asks for.

"His meritorious acts and austere penances have made him invincible and no one is capable of defeating him in battle. I am practically helpless and cannot save you, but I have not lost hope. We should all go to see Lord Vishnu. He is our preserver, and he will definitely find a way to help you regain your abode."

$\mathcal{T}$aking Lord Brahma with them as their leader, the gods went to Kshir Sagar (the ocean of milk) where Lord Vishnu, preserver of the world, was resting on his serpent Shesha's coiled body. His wife, Lakshmi, was, as usual, giving him a foot massage.

The very sight of Lord Vishnu was a great relief. The gods cried out to him, "Save us, Lord! Save us from the tyranny of Bali! We have been driven out of our home. We have no food. You alone can save us from King Bali's reign of terror."

$\mathcal{L}$ord Vishnu understood the sorry plight of the gods and tired to console them. "Cast off your fears," Lord Vishnu said. "I will definitely find a way to get you back your home and your glory. I cannot defeat Bali in battle because his penances, disciplined life, meritorious acts of charity, and the adherence to the path of virtue have made him invincible. The only way to conquer Bali is to trick him. I will disguise myself as a dwarf, born from the womb of Aditi, mother of the gods. Using my intelligence, I will trick Bali to get back your homeland and free the Earth so that human beings can once again make offerings to you. Do not lose courage," Lord Vishnu told them. "Have faith and go back to your shelters."

At an opportune moment, Lord Vishnu took birth as the dwarf Brahmachari. His parents, mother Aditi and Rishni Kashyap, reveled in his angelic appearance. The gods quickly recognized the bright dwarf as an incarnation of Lord Vishnu and began worshiping him.

Shukracharya, the guru of the demons, became aware of this new incarnation of Vishnu through his meditation and rushed into the private apartment of King Bali to tell him about Vishnu's intentions.

"Lord Vishnu has taken birth as the dwarf Brahmachari and is on his way to trick you to obtain back the kingdom of Swarga Loka for the gods and Bhu Loka for humans," Shukracharya said. "Do not, O King, be deceived by his false form. He will be coming as a beggar because he knows of your vow of charity. But you cannot give charity to enemies. Please do not give him any alms."

Bali was unconcerned by this news. He said he was

honored that Vishnu, the unchallenged Lord of the three worlds, was coming to him as a beggar to beg. "Let him come and beg anytime he wants. I cannot break my vow. I am obliged to give whatever is asked of me and is within my domain. I am sorry Shukracharya, my most respectable teacher, I cannot refuse Vishnu. Yet I am thankful to you for bringing me this information."

Shukracharya pleaded, "Vishnu is a famous trickster. He will deceive you, O King, and you will be deprived of all your belongings. He will make you helpless. As your teacher, I beg you to listen to my advice and save yourself from the disaster that Vishnu brings for you."

"No," said Bali. "I have made a vow of charity. I will not hesitate even if Vishnu asks for my life. I will not break my vow. As my teacher, it is your duty to help me keep my word."

"Then do as you please," Shukracharya said. "Whatever is destined will happen. Who can stop it? I only followed my dharma and warned you. Now you must follow your dharma and do as your conscience guides you."

After some time, when Bali was sitting on his throne and all his ministers and Guru Shukracharya were in their respective asanas (seats), the dwarf Brahmachari appeared in Bali's presence. The ministers and Guru Shukracharya were so overwhelmed by Brahmachari's divine presence that they all stood up to welcome the young Brahmin boy, who arrived in the assembly hall with a bewitching smile.

King Bali immediately recognized Brahmachari as Lord Vishnu and asked, "What brings you here sir?" "O respected King, I am a young Brahmin student with no place to live. I need a place to erect a little hut, where I can continue my studies unobstructed. I need very little land, only as much land as I can cover with my little feet in three steps so that I can build my own place."

"Ask me for more, young man. I am king of three worlds. Three steps of land mean nothing to me."

"Thank you for your generosity, but the little piece of land that I have asked for would be more than enough to me," Brahmachari said. "Please just make the samkalpa and allow me to measure three footsteps from your vast kingdom."

King Bali left his throne and asked for the kamandalu (waterpot) to perform the samkalpa, which is done before all acts of charity. Afraid that the king would complete the samkalpa ritual, Shukracharya sipped some water from the kamandalu to become small enough to enter the spout of the kamandalu to prevent the flow of the water. Aware of Shukracharya's actions, Brahmachari forced a piece of straw into the neck of the kamandalu to clear the passage. The straw pierced through the eye of Shukracharya who, unable to bear the pain, jumped out of the pot, allowing the water to start flowing again. King Bali sipped the water from the kamandalu three times, chanting the mantra that repeated his intention to give three footsteps of land to Brahmachari. After the ritual was over, King Bali asked the dwarf Brahmachari to measure the land. Soon after Bali's request the dwarf started increasing his size and became unbelievably large. In his first step Brahmachari

measured the entire Earth, with all its rivers, mountains, and oceans. In his second step he measured all seven lokas and his foot even reached up to the abode of Lord Brahma, known as Brahma Loka.

When Lord Brahma saw the extended foot of what was really Lord Vishnu, disguised as Brahmachari, crossing all the lokas and reaching up to his own abode, he became excited. "This will never happen again," Lord Brahma thought to himself. "Never again will Vishnu put all his energy into his one foot. I must preserve this energy," Lord Brahma said, and he began to contemplate a way he could accomplish this feat. Lord Brahma decided that when the big toe of the left foot of Lord Vishnu came in his direction he would wash it with the water from his kamandalu and then store the water in which Vishnu's toe was washed back in his kamandalu.

The water Lord Brahma was able to obtain from washing Lord Vishnu's foot was like an elixir. It was from this magical elixir that, in due course of time, a beautiful girl was born. The girl was adopted by Lord Brahma as his daughter and was given the name Ganga.

$\mathcal{M}$eanwhile, after measuring all the lokas above the Earth, Lord Vishnu, still disguised as Brahmachari, asked, "Where should I put my third step, O King? The entire Earth and Heaven has been measured by me in only two steps. You still owe me whatever land I would measure in my third step."

"You should put your third step on my head, O Lord," King Bali replied with great humility. "That is all I can offer. I have nothing more left."

Lord Vishnu put his left foot on Bali's head and pressed down with a tremendous force. King Bali's entire body sank into the Earth, reaching all the way down to Patal Loka, the Underworld, and Bali asked Vishnu to promise to live in Patal Loka as his guard. Thus Vishnu freed Heaven and Earth from Bali's domain.

The gods were happy because they got back their abode. The humans were happy to again have the freedom to worship the gods of their choice. And King Bali was happy because he would get the company of Lord Vishnu, even if it was confined to the Underworld.

Ganga in Heaven

The young and charming Ganga made life for the dwellers of Brahma Loka lots of fun through her playful nature, her music, and her dance. She was a happy girl, and she enjoyed living in Brahma Loka. Ganga also had free passage to all the other lokas, and she brought joy and happiness to everyone wherever she went.

All the love and admiration showered on her by Lord Brahma and all the other gods made Ganga a little arrogant and high-handed, but her beauty, charm, and lighthearted nature compelled the gods to overlook this minor part of her behavior.

One day when Ganga was in Swarga Loka with Lord Brahma, Indra, Varun, and Kuber, the great sage Durvasa happened to visit. Rishi Durvasa has always been famous for getting easily agitated and angry. Everyone tries to be very careful when around him so that he remains in a good mood, otherwise he will curse whoever causes him annoyance.

While Durvasa was strolling around Swarga Loka, a gust of wind came and blew off the only cloth with which he was wrapped. As Durvasa was trying to put the cloth back on his body to avoid being naked, the wind kept pulling the cloth away. Ganga saw Rishi Durvasa's struggle and began to giggle. All the other gods who were present turned their faces away out of respect. Rishi Durvasa became furious when he heard Ganga's laughter and saw that she was enjoying his struggle to keep himself covered. After the wind died down, Durvasa wrapped himself back in his cloth and then addressed Ganga.

"Ganga you are disrespectful. You mock saints, and you are a disgrace to the dwellers of the higher lokas. You will have to leave Heaven and the higher lokas and dwell on Earth as a river. When the humans wash their dirty linen in your water, you will realize how privileged you have been to be able to dwell in Swarga Loka."

Everyone was shocked by Durvasa's curse. They respectfully asked Durvasa to pardon Ganga for her childish behavior, but Durvasa remained adamant and said, "My curse cannot be revoked. Ganga will have to descend to Earth to pay for her disobedience."

Ganga realized she had behaved badly, and she asked Durvasa to set a fixed time for her punishment so that she could return to Swarga Loka after the period of punishment was over. Durvasa, after considering her request, said, "When your water becomes polluted you may come back to Swarga Loka again. As long as your water remains pure, you will have to remain on Earth. Now that you have become respectful you in turn will get respect from the people on Earth. They will worship you for your purifying quality."

*R*ishi Durvasa left Swarga Loka and everyone was very sad because they did not want Ganga to leave them. The news of Durvasa's curse spread like jungle fire, and soon the eight vasus (the guardian angels of the eight directions) heard about Ganga's punishment.

The eight vasus came to see Ganga and said, "Devi Ganga, Rishi Durvasa has cursed you and is now sending you to Earth. Will you please help us while you are on Earth?"

Ganga did not understand how she could help the vasus since she knew nothing about their lives. She asked them exactly what kind of help they needed from her. The Vasus then told her the story of their own curse, punishment for when they stole Sage Vashishtha's cow.

age Vashishtha was the mind-born son of Lord Brahma. Vashishtha had a wish-fulfilling cow named Surabhi that was capable of producing anything that anybody wanted. Vashishtha was able to manage all the needs of his family and his ashram dwellers through the help of this cow. No one had to work, and they all had time for study, meditation, and performing rituals.

"One day," the vasus said, "we went with our wives to the site of Rishi Vashishtha's ashram and saw this wish-fulfilling cow. We were amazed by its limitless power to satisfy all kinds of desires. Our wives loved it very much, and one of them suggested that we should steal the cow and take it with us to enjoy its benefits. Under pressure from his wife, one of us became so taken by the idea that he convinced us all to steal the cow. Soon Rishi Vashishtha discovered the cow was missing and he cursed us for our act of stealing. He said to us, 'You are responsible vasus. You are the guardians of all living beings, and yet you are doing this unvirtuous act of stealing. You should all be born

as human beings on Earth to confront the miseries of human life.'

"After this curse," the vasus said, "we became very sad, and the fear of being born as mortals overtook us. We are still waiting to find a way we can be born on Earth as mortals but can be released from the bondage of our human bodies as soon as possible. And this is how you can help us," they explained to Ganga. "When you go to Earth you can give birth to us and become our mother. Then you can release us from our mortal human bodies by drowning us in your deep waters."

Ganga, after giving it some thought, said, "I promise I will help you as much as possible. However, the one of you who really stole the cow will have to stay on Earth to face the miseries of human incarnation. The rest of you I will release from your mortal bodies without any delay as soon as you are born."

"We will all wait for the opportune moment," said the vasus, and then they departed.

$\mathcal{G}$anga was still sad that she was cursed, but now she was also happy. She realized she would have a new life where she would flow freely and help liberate the tormented souls on Earth from the bondage of their karmas. She realized she would be an instrument in purifying countless souls.

Despite all these events, there was no immediate need for Ganga to descend to Earth. So she continued to live in Swarga Loka and visit in the other lokas, waiting for the moment when she would be called by human beings to go to Earth as their liberator.

Time passed

The Story of King Sagar

The moment when Ganga was needed came when King Sagar of the Solar Dynasty on Earth decided to perform an Ashwamedh Yagya (horse sacrifice) in order to become Emperor of the Earth. The Ashwamedh Yagya is always performed by kings when they want sovereignty over neighboring kingdoms. As part of this yagya, a homa is performed by priests and sages. At the end of the ceremony, a horse, well decorated with costly ornaments, is worshiped and let loose to go in any direction he chooses. An army, complete with generals, is sent with the horse to see that the horse is able to move freely in his chosen direction. When the horse enters into neighboring kingdoms, the people in these kingdoms either have to accept the sovereignty of the king performing the Ashwamedh Yagya or they have to capture the horse and challenge the authority of the king expanding his dominion. This naturally results in a war between the army guarding the horse and those in the kingdom who obstruct the path of the horse. If the people choose not to fight then they must present gifts to the army that are then delivered to the conquering king as a sign of the new king.

King Sagar had sixty thousand and one sons and a very large army. No king dared challenge his authority and his horse traveled unobstructed through all the neighboring countries. King Sagar was well on his way to becoming the Chakravarti King (the Emperor of Earth).

$\mathcal{I}$ndra, The king of Heaven, saw the triumph of King Sagar over all the kings of Earth and became scared. He thought that if Sagar became the unchallenged king of Earth that he would also be entitled to the throne of Indra. Indra decided to obstruct Sagar's Ashwamedh Yagya.

Now unless the horse performing the Ashwamedh Yagya returns to its place of origin, the ritual is not considered complete. So Indra stole Sagar's horse and took it to the ashram of the great Sage Kapil, a far-off place near the Bay of Bengal that was below the earth's surface and hidden from the view of humans at that time. Thus Indra destroyed King Sagar's dream to become the Chakravarti King, the Sovereign of the Earth.

*I*ndra tied the horse to a tree behind the back of Sage Kapil. Sage Kapil was in Samadhi, the deepest state of meditation, and so did not see the mischief Indra was up to.

Sagar's army was very disturbed when it could not see the horse, and it started searching in all directions. The part of the army led by the sons of Sagar came to a large canyon, which they climbed down into to search for the horse but encountered instead a huge elephant. This elephant is the animal that helps maintain the balance of the Earth, and it is known by the name Diggaj (*dig* or *dik* means direction; *gaj* means elephant). There are eight directions on the Earth—north, northeast, south, southeast and so on—and there are eight elephants, one in each of these directions, that keep the Earth in balance. The chief of the army asked the elephant in the canyon about the missing horse and the elephant expressed his ignorance, but he suggested the army follow the canyon to the south, all the way to the end of the Earth. So the sons of Sagar and the army moved southward until they arrived at the ashram of Sage Kapil.

When the army and the sons of Sagar reached the ashram of Sage Kapil, they found Sagar's horse tied to the trunk of a tree behind Kapil's back. The army chief and the sons of Sagar became angry when they saw Sage Kapil sitting in meditation. They used abusive language and called the great sage a thief. Even though they could see that the rishi was in meditation, they thought he was trying to fool them by pretending to be in Samadhi, the deepest state of meditation. They were convinced that Sage Kapil had stolen the horse and brought it to his ashram, where no one could find it. They called him a phony, a thief, and mischievous, and their voices were filled with anger and disgust.

Rishi Kapil was in fact in Samadhi, and the awful sounds that broke his meditation caused him to open his eyes in rage. Yoga agni (yoga fire) came out from his eyes and all sixty thousand sons and the accompanying army were burned. All that remained of Sagar's army and his sixty thousand sons were heaps of ashes on the ground.

Time passed and King Sagar had received no news about his sons, his army, or his sacrificial horse. He became worried. The Ashwamedh Yagya could not be completed without the return of the horse, so Sagar asked his only remaining son, Anshuman, to go and find out what had happened.

Anshuman set out for the journey and went all the way to the ashram of Rishi Kapil where he found Sagar's horse tied to a tree and the sage in meditation. Anshuman sat down on the ground near a heap of ashes and waited for Kapil to regain his normal state of consciousness.

After some time, the rishi opened his eyes and saw Anshuman waiting patiently for him. The rishi asked Anshuman why he was there, and Anshuman explained who he was and the purpose of his visit. Kapil told Anshuman the part of the story he knew and showed Anshuman the heap of ashes that was lying near him and said, "So my son, your army and your brothers have been consumed by my yoga agni. You should take your horse and go back to your father. He can complete the Ashwamedh Yagya if he likes."

"What about my brothers?" asked Anshuman.

"Their time is over," said Rishi Kapil.

"But Sire," said Anshuman, "when somebody dies a natural death he gets another birth of Nirvana, heaven, or hell, according to his karmas. But when somebody dies because of a curse that person remains in the form of a ghost and can never be liberated unless something is done to undo the curse. Tell me, Rishi, how I may free my brothers' souls from your curse. Please be kind and suggest some way to save the souls of my brothers."

"There is only one remedy," Kapil said, "but it is a difficult task. You must bring Ganga to Earth from Heaven. Only the holy water of Ganga is capable of purifying and liberating the souls of your brothers and your army."

"What must I do to bring Ganga to Earth? I know nothing about Ganga. Please tell me something about Ganga," Anshuman said with folded hands.

"Ganga was born from the holy water in Lord Brahma's kamandalu—water that Lord Brahma obtained by washing the holy feet of Lord Vishnu when Vishnu was in his dwarf incarnation as Brahmachari," Kapil told Anshuman. "Because Ganga was born from that holy water, she has the power to purify any object that touches her holy water. At present Ganga dwells in Swarga Loka and the other upper lokas, but by pleasing Lord Brahma with austere penances you could obtain her as a boon and bring her to Earth."

Anshuman thanked Sage Kapil, took the horse, and went back with a heavy heart to his father's kingdom. He met his father and his father's ministers at the gates of the city.

King Sagar was deeply saddened by Anshuman's news. Sagar decided to hand over his kingdom to Anshuman, his only remaining son, and went to the forest to invoke Lord Brahma, the creator of the universe, in order to bring Ganga to Earth. Unable to achieve this goal, Sagar left his mortal body.

*I*n due course of time Anshuman handed over the kingdom to his son and went to the forest to perform penances to invoke Lord Brahma. Anshuman also could not achieve this goal and left his mortal body.

Now this pattern became a routine of the kings of the Sagar Dynasty. Each king ruled until his son became responsible enough to run the kingdom and then the king would inform his heir about the task to be fulfilled, retire to the forest, and worship rigorously to invoke Lord Brahma.

In the seventh generation of King Sagar was born a boy whose name was Bhagirath. Bhagirath was called by his father when his father was on his death bed and told about the responsibility of fulfilling the task that one after another of his ancestors had not been able to fulfill. Bhagirath made a promise to his father, saying, "I will invoke Lord Brahma and bring the divine river Ganga to Earth. Do not worry, O Father. I will get the sins of my ancestors eradicated."

*B*hagirath then left his throne and crown in the charge of his wise and honest ministers and went to the forest. He entered a state of Sadhma, a deep, austere, and highly disciplined worship. He sat like a rishi under a tree, completely absorbed in his meditation of Lord Brahma. His looks changed. His beard and hairs grew, and his body started glowing from the radiance produced by his austerities.

Lord Brahma was pleased with Bhagirath's tapas (penance) and appeared to him in person, saying, "Bhagirath, my son, I am happy with you. You have achieved what your ancestors have been trying to achieve for many years. Ask me for your desired boon."

"Grandsire, my ancestors have been invoking you for several generations because we need Ganga to come to Earth. Her holy water alone can eradicate the sins of our ancestors who were burned to ashes by Sage Kapil. Please bestow upon us the purifying Ganga who resides in your kamandalu."

"I have no objection to releasing Ganga," Lord Brahma said, "but if I simply release her from my kamandalu the force with which she will descend will overwhelm the Earth. You will have to worship Lord Shiva first. When Lord Shiva agrees to hold the horrendous force of Ganga in his matted hairs then I will be glad to release her." After saying this Lord Brahma disappeared and Bhagirath began another severe penance.

*N*ow to invoke Lord Shiva, Bhagirath stood on the big toe of his left leg and prayed. After he became absorbed in the name of Lord Shiva by constant japa (repetition) of the mantra "Aum Namah Shivaye," Lord Shiva appeared before Bhagirath.

"Open your eyes, dear son Bhagirath," said Lord Shiva. "I am pleased with your austere penance. Tell me what you want from me. I will be more than happy to do it for you."

Bhagirath opened his eyes and paid his homage to Lord Shiva. He explained what Lord Brahma had told him and requested Lord Shiva to hold the forcefully descending Ganga in his matted hairlocks. Lord Shiva assured Bhagirath that he would help him, so Bhagirath went back to Lord Brahma. He told Lord Brahma about the promise of Lord Shiva and requested that Lord Brahma release Ganga to Earth.

Lord Brahma asked Ganga to go to Earth now that she was needed there, but Ganga refused to go. She argued that the abundance of sins committed by humans that she would have to carry upon reaching the Earth was too great. She said, "People will wash their impure bodies and put their waste material in my pure water, and I will become polluted."

Lord Brahma assured her that she would remain pure and instead would wash away the impurities of all who came in contact with her water. "Their souls will get purified," Lord Brahma said, "and they will remember you with devotion."

But Ganga was hesitant. The Kali Yuga was coming. Humans were going to be crazy after the gratification of their senses. They would destroy all of nature and, in the end, the Earth.

Lord Brahma said, "Well Ganga, despite your fears, you still have to go to Earth anyway because of the curse of Rishi Durvasa. Also you have to liberate the vasus, as you promised, so you have more than enough reasons to go to Earth. Why hesitate? Go, and when your water becomes polluted come back."

Ganga had no choice. She had to accept Lord Brahma's command. Lord Brahma then said to Bhagirath, "Go to Kailsh, Bhagirath, my dear son, and tell Lord Shiva that Ganga will soon descend from Heaven to Earth. He will need to hold back her force before she touches the Earth.

Bhagirath happily returned to Lord Shiva and told him the auspicious news. Lord Shiva selected a suitable spot to receive Ganga and stood waiting for Ganga's descent.

Ganga started her descent toward Earth with full force. Lord Shiva spread his hairlocks and covered the entire sky. Then, with a jerk, he shook his hairlocks and tied them on his head.

The size of Lord Shiva's hairlocks was so big that Ganga, with all her waves, was easily captured. Not a drop of water came to Earth. Ganga was still flowing with tremendous force inside Shiva's hairlocks, but the water could not escape. Ganga became helpless. She felt like a prisoner in Lord Shiva's hairlocks.

After Ganga calmed down and her mind was at peace, Shiva sat down in his favorite posture and went into blissful Samadhi.

Bhagirath wondered what was going to happen next. He wanted Ganga to come with him to the place where the ashes of his ancestors were lying, but Ganga was now caught in the hairlocks of Shiva.

He went to Lord Shiva and pleaded, "Lord, now that Ganga is under your complete control, please release her gently from your hairlocks and instruct her to follow me to my ancestors' ashes at Sage Kapil's ashram."

Shiva assured Bhagirath that he would release Ganga for his holy job, and then Shiva asked Ganga to follow Bhagirath to the ashram of Sage Kapil.

"My dear son," Lord Shiva said to Bhagirath, "you may now lead Ganga to your ancestors' ashes. Blow your conch shell to clear the way. She will follow you." Saying this, Lord Shiva released Ganga by squeezing one of his hairlocks.

*F*reed from the hairlocks of Shiva, Ganga, in the form of a beautiful maiden, stood with her hands folded in front of Lord Shiva. After paying homage to him, she bid Lord Shiva farewell and started following Bhagirath, who was moving forward blowing his conch shell.

Wherever she walked, the touch of Ganga brought new life to the plants and vegetables in her path.

Bhagirath was moving toward Sage Kapil's ashram, but before he could get out of the mountain area he reached the ashram of Rishi Janu.

Rishi Janu was performing a yagya (fire worship), and the people at his ashram were chanting mantras. Ganga became curious. She had never heard a group of human beings chanting mantras before so she decided to see for herself what was happening.

When Ganga entered the ashram of Rishi Janu the ashram became flooded. Her water rushed in and extinguished the holy fire, and the pooja pots (pots used in worship) started to float away. The people were frightened. They all ran toward a high spot under a huge tree. Rishi Janu became really angry. Through his meditation he understood exactly what was happening.

"So, Ganga has come down from Heaven," he murmured. "She is proud of herself and her power, but she does not know how to behave near an ashram. She has no respect for human beings. She also does not yet know the powers of a rishi. I must teach her a lesson."

The rishi then chanted a mantra and took a sip of Ganga water. With the power of his mantra, the entire body of Ganga and all her water were swallowed by the rishi. All traces of Ganga were gone.

*B*hagirath was totally unaware of this whole affair. He was still moving forward blowing his conch shell. When he turned back to see if Ganga was following him, he found that Ganga was not there. He remembered that she was behind him up until the ashram of Rishi Janu. So he went back to Janu's ashram and found the rishi sitting under a tree.

Bhagirath saw the pots and pans lying all over the ground. He knew something had happened, but he didn't know what. He prostrated in front of the rishi and told him the whole story of his journey. Then he inquired about Ganga.

The rishi heard the story and knew of its truth by his divine sight. Janu felt pity for Bhagirath, who had worked so hard to bring Ganga to Earth. Now Ganga was trapped inside Janu's body. Rishi Janu consoled Bhagirath and said, "For you, Bhagirath, I will release Ganga immediately," and saying this he made a cut in his left thigh, and Ganga water flew out from that opening like a fountain. Soon the body of water assumed the form of the divine maiden Ganga, who now also wanted to thank the rishi. She said, "I was pure because I was born from the pure Vishnu energy in Lord Brahma's kamandalu. I was further purified by staying on Lord Shiva's head. Now I am again purified and energized by your energy, Rishi Janu, which you earned by leading an austere life. My purifying power has increased and from now on I will be known as your daughter Janhvi, after your name. I ask that you please bless Bhagirath to successfully fulfill his mission and liberate the souls of his ancestors from the curse of Rishi Kapil."

Rishi Janu blessed both Ganga and Bhagirath to be able to reach their desired goal without any more obstacles in the future.

Soon after leaving Rishi Janu's ashram, Ganga and Bhagirath came down to the plains of north India and made their way toward Sage Kapil's ashram.

Wherever Ganga went and through whichever area she flowed, people came in large numbers and the places became filled with a spiritual atmosphere. The people bathed, offered oblations to their ancestors, chanted mantras, and enjoyed the presence of Ganga.

Finally Ganga, led by Bhagirath, reached the ashram of Sage Kapil. Sage Kapil was overwhelmed with joy at Ganga's arrival. He welcomed her and led Ganga to the spot where the ashes were lying. Bhagirath stood with his hands folded in adoration. As soon as Ganga touched the ashes of King Sagar's sons and soldiers, they came out of the waves of Ganga in their astral bodies, glowing with divine light. They were all praying to Ganga and ascending toward the higher lokas. At the same time the ancestors of Bhagirath who were already in Heaven came in their respective viman (diving air crafts) to watch this long-awaited moment. Bhagirath had done what none of them was able to accomplish, and they all showered flowers on Bhagirath in gratitude.

Sage Kapil blessed the spot where all this happened because if the sons of Sagar had not been burned here by Kapil's yoga agni, Ganga would never have come to flow at this place on Earth. "This place," Kapil said, "will be known as Ganga Sagar. It is here that Ganga will merge with the Sagar (ocean). Those who come on this day to bathe at the meeting point of Ganga and the Sagar will not only be purified but even their ancestors will be purified and will enjoy the blissful life of Heaven."

*L*ord Brahma also appeared at this special occasion and said, "Son Bhagirath, you devoted your entire life to the welfare of your ancestors. You did not enjoy your youth and you did not have any children to carry on your lineage or your name. From this day forward Ganga will be known as Bhagirathi so that your name shall always remain in the mortal world. Ganga will purify the entire population of human beings who bathe in her water or use her water in any way. And she herself will be purified by the saints who will bathe in her water. Thus she will remain pure as long as there are saints in the world."

And from that day until this, Ganga continues to flow gracefully from the Himalayas to the shores of the Bay of Bengal where she merges with the ocean. The entire route of her flow is dotted with numerous holy sites and temples. People from all over India worship her as a mother goddess who washes away sins and liberates them from the human cycle of birth and death. All those who read this story or who remember Ganga with devotion will be purified.

ITI Shri Gangaye Namah

The Ganga Stotram prayer that appears in Sanskrit on the facing pages was composed by Shankaracharya in A.D.500 to express his gratitude for all that Ganga does. Hindus chant this prayer in Sanskrit whenever they wish to pray to Ganga.

Below is a summary of the prayer, not a direct translation. In order for *The Ganga Stotram* to have the desired effect, it must be chanted in Sanskrit, just like a mantra.

You are the purifier of the three worlds. Your life-giving water cures evil thoughts and deeds and provides perfect peace of mind. I humbly pray to your lotus feet.

You gave Bhagirath his desired boon and your power to purify is known throughout the three worlds. I am not able to comprehend your might. Excuse me for my shortcomings and ignorance.

You were born from the holy feet of Lord Vishnu and were placed by Lord Shiva in the beautiful snow-clad Himalayas. The droplets of your pure water are like pearls. Those who live near your banks attain salvation.

You are adored by all—in all three worlds.

I am your humble servant, the composer of this hymn. Whoever recites this hymn will achieve whatever he or she wants.

॥ गङ्गास्तोत्रम् ॥

देवि सुरेश्वरि भगवति गङ्गे त्रिभुवनतारिणि तरल तरङ्गे ।
शङ्कर मौलिविहारिणि विमले मम मतिरास्तां तव पदकमले ॥ १ ॥

भागीरथि सुखदायिनि मातस्तव जलमहिमा निगमे ख्यातः ।
नाहं जाने तव महिमानं त्राहि कृपामयि मामज्ञानम् ॥ २ ॥

हरिपद पद्म तरङ्गिणि गङ्गे हिमविधिमुक्ताधवल तरङ्गे ।
दूरी कुरु मम दुष्कृति भारं कुरु कृपया भवसागर पारम् ॥ ३ ॥

तव जलममलं येन निपीतं परमपदं खलु तेन गृहीतम् ।
मातर्गङ्गे त्वयि यो भक्तः किल तं द्रष्टुं न यमः शक्तः ॥ ४ ॥

पतितोद्धारिणि जाह्नवि गङ्गे खण्डितगिरिवरमण्डित भङ्गे ।
भीष्मजननि हे मुनिवरकन्ये पतितनिवारिणि त्रिभुवन धन्ये ॥ ५ ॥

कल्पलतामिव फलदां लोके प्रणमति यस्त्वां न पतति शोके ।
पारावारविहारिणि गङ्गे विमुख युवति कृत तरलापाङ्गे ॥ ६ ॥

तव कृपया चेत् स्रोतः स्नातः पुनरपि जठरे सोऽपि न जातः ।
नरक निवारिणि जाह्नवी गङ्गे कलुष विनाशिनि महिमोत्तुङ्गे ॥ ७ ॥

परिल सदङ्गे पुण्यतरङ्गे जय जय जाह्नवि करुणा पाङ्गे ।
इन्द्र मुकुटमणि राजित चरणे सुखदे शुभदे सेवकशरणे ॥ ८ ॥

रोगं शोकं तापं पापं हर मे भगवति कुमतिकलापम् ।
त्रिभुवन सारे वसुधा हारे त्वमसि गतिर्मम खलु संसारे ॥ ९ ॥

अलकानन्दे परमानन्दे कुरु मयि करुणां कातर वन्द्ये ।
तव तट निकटे यस्य हि वासः खलु वैकुण्ठे तस्य निवासः ॥ १० ॥

वरमिह नीरे कमठो मीनः किं वा तीरे सरटः क्षीणः ।
अथवा श्वपचो मलिनो दीनः न च तव दूर नृपतिकुलीनः ॥ ११ ॥

भो भुवनेश्वरी पुण्ये धन्ये देवि द्रवमयि मुनिवर कन्ये ।
गङ्गास्तवमिदममलं नित्यं पठति नरो यः स जयति सत्यम् ॥ १२ ॥

येषाम्ह्रदये गङ्गा भक्तिस्तेषां भवति सदा सुख मुक्तिः ।
मधुर मनोहरपज्झटिकाभिः परमानन्दाकर ललिताभिः ॥ १३ ॥

गङ्गा स्तोत्रमिदं भवसारं वाञ्छित फलदं विगतिशतभारम् ।
शङ्कर सेवक शङ्कर रचितं पठतु च विषयीकृत चित्तम् ॥ १४ ॥

Aum Shri Ganeshaye Namah

About the Illustrations

After paying my homage to Lord Ganesh I bow down to the holy feet of my teacher Shri Chandra Bal through whose training I was able to learn the technique of wash painting. My teacher himself learned it from Shri Bhawani Prasad Mittal, who learned it at Shamti Niketan, where he studied art.

All forty-six illustrations in *The Birth of the Ganga* are wash paintings on silk. The description that follows is my first attempt to explain in writing how this style of painting is done.

Wash painting is a special technique of painting in which both watercolor and tempera are used to create the desired effect. Watercolors are used in their pure form and opaque white or black are avoided until the last step of the painting (see step 7 below) or are not used at all. The watercolors are applied the same way as in a watercolor painting, but a special technique of fixing colors is used that the painters of pure watercolor do not use.

There are eight steps in creating one painting:

1. Draw or line the entire drawing with dark color lines and then fill in these outlines with lighter colors. This technique is useful in coloring any figure or for creating any mood. For instance, if the trousers should be yellow, then the line drawing of the trousers is done with orange, which is deeper than the yellow that will be used to fill in the trousers. If the body of the figure drawn is going to be brown, the line drawing of the body should be made with the deeper tone of burnt sienna, which can be darkened by adding a touch of Prussian blue. If the scroll the figure is carrying has to be white, the line drawing of the scroll should be done in cobalt blue.

In the face, the eyebrows and eyes should be lined by Prussian blue. In lining the lips, one should use carmine in the upper lip and vermilion for the lower lip. The nose and ears should be lined with the dark tone of the color used in the face. If the hair is supposed to be golden, the line drawing of the hair should be done in yellow ochre. If the hair is supposed to be black, the lining should be done in Prussian blue.

2. Before filling in the colors, the line drawing should be fixed by pouring water over the painted surface. Whenever colors are applied to art paper or a silk canvas, they are partly absorbed by the paper or silk. In the fixing process, the extra color that does not penetrate the canvas or paper is washed off. The painted paper or silk is either floated in a tray full of water or it is placed on a wooden board and then water is poured on the board in such a way that the water does not fall directly on the painting but floats over the painting and rinses off the extra color. When clear water starts running from the board then the pouring of the water is stopped. Then the painting is allowed to dry on the board. A brush should not be used to remove the overflowing colors. The colors should flow out from the painting only by pouring the water. The fixing process is repeated each time color is applied to the painting. If the painting happens to be made on silk, one should use water in which a few soap-nuts have been boiled for the fixing. (Soap-nuts also should be added to the water used to dissolve or thin the colors used in painting.) A silk canvas should be gently stretched on the drawing board on which the fixing is done so there are no wrinkles or bubbles.

3. After the canvas is completely dry, all the figures and forms that have been drawn should be filled in with color. Every color should be used in three tones: highlight, middle tone, and depth.

The color of the middle tone should be selected first, and then water is added to this color to make the highlight color. The color for depth is obtained by mixing a darker tone to the color of the middle tone. The color chosen for the middle tone will be the visible color of the drawing.

4. The colors used to fill in the painting should be fixed by the same process that was used for fixing the line drawing.

5. Then color should be applied to the background. The corners of the painting should be a darker tone of the color used for the background.

6. After the background is colored, the painting should be fixed again to stabilize the background color.

7. Now comes the wash part of the painting. The artist should think about the mood that the painting represents and what colors will best present the

environment the artist wishes to create—the effect of day, night, or any desired time and the effect of the season.

The colors used for giving a wash are not watercolors; they are tempera and are opaque. The use of white is quite liberal during the wash phase, whereas white is avoided prior to this point. Three tones of each wash color should be made, as in step 3: highlight, middle tone, and depth. The artist may use as many colors as he or she likes to wash the painting.

After the wash colors have been prepared, the painting should be made wet with water. Because the colors have already been fixed, no color will come out of the painting. Any excess water should be allowed to drip off the painting before the wash is applied.

The wash should not be too thick or too thin. It should be between the consistency of thin honey and boiled milk. When the wash is applied, the entire painting should appear as if it is behind colored fog or clouds. The corners should contain the darkest area of the wash color.

Before the wash step is completed, the artist should take a dry brush and remove the wash color from the face, hands, and feet of any figures in the painting. The wash color must still be wet when the color from the face, hands, and feet is removed. Once the paint starts to dry it is too late for this step. The painting should be left in a position so that any extra wash may flow off while the painting is drying.

8. After the painting is completely dry, the wash color needs to be fixed. As in step 2, water is poured over the entire painted surface and any extra color rinses off.

If the desired effect for the final painting comes in one wash, there is no need to repeat this step, and the finishing of the painting can then proceed. If the colors are not the proper tones, shade, consistency, or if they have washed off from certain areas, then the artist should start all eight steps over again. The artist should approach the work as if it is the first time he or she is working on the painting.

The artist should:

1) Do the lining of the drawing with the same colors as before.
2) Fix the line drawing.
3) Fill in the colors.
4) Fix the colors of the painted figures.

5) Color the background.

6) Fix the colors of the background.

7) Give a wash with one color, or as many colors as the artist thinks are needed, and remove the wash color from the face, hands, and feet of the figures before the colors dry.

8) Fix the colors applied in the wash.

One can feel the difference in the appearance of a painting after it has received two washes, and the wash process can be repeated if a stronger wash effect is desired. Some of the paintings in *The Birth of the Ganga* received more than four washes, and most of them received at least four washes.

Now the painting is ready for finishing.

The beauty of Indian art lies in its delicate line work. In Western art colors and tones define the division of space but that is not the case in these wash paintings. In finishing wash paintings we repeat the lining of the face, fingers, toes, dresses, and ornaments with the depth color. The face is finished by applying color to the lining of the eyebrows, eyelids, eyes, nose, lips, ears, and chin. The upper lip is always made darker than the lower lip. In areas where greater depth is needed, such as near all joints and folds, additional depth lines are added.

The painting will now start reappearing from within the clouds of wash. To maintain the effect of the wash, the figures and everything else drawn on the painting should fade and merge with the background near the extremities of the painting.

Now I will describe the forms and figures that have been used in *The Birth of the Ganga* paintings. The style of the figures in this book is a mixture of three existing forms of Indian artwork that can be found in the painted or sculptured art forms in temples throughout India.

The faces—specifically the eyes, nose, and lips—and the hands and feet are drawn in the style of the paintings located in the Ajanta caves. They represent a two-thousand-year-old fresco style of artwork.

The proportions used in the figures are like those of the sculptures in the Elephanta caves near Bombay. These proportions were chosen because they are so beautiful and delicate, unlike the proportions found in the Ajanta cave paintings, which are very heavy and result in dwarflike figures. The sculptures in the Elephanta caves represent a style that is thousands of years older than the familiar Rajasthan style of artwork that is generally recognized as Indian art.

The postures and movements shown in *The Birth of the Ganga* artwork were inspired by the ancient sculptures of the Ellora caves and the Khajoraho temple because of the grace, preciseness, and expressiveness that these sculptures exemplify.

Another important feature of the artwork in *The Birth of the Ganga* is the rich use of hand postures. There are not more than ten hand postures that are generally drawn by artists throughout the world. Indian art, however, uses as many as sixty-four hand postures, reflecting the sixty-four hand postures used in Indian dance rituals and worship. These hand postures, or mudras, have their own symbolism and language and are used as a way to express emotions. The richness that is found in the hand postures of Indian art is a gift to the entire world. The artwork shown in *The Birth of the Ganga* uses these hand postures as a language of the heart as opposed to the language of the head.

Ehud C. Sperling, the publisher of this book, was the one who introduced the idea of illustrating the story of Ganga in wash paintings. No one realized how much work it would be to create nearly fifty paintings, but the work went very smoothly thanks to the dedications, hard work, and persistence of Pieter Weltevrede, who has been my student for more than eighteen years.

My own teacher, Shri Chandra Bal, guided Pieter in choosing the wash colors to bring the feelings of the paints to a visual level. And although I helped with the compositions, color setting, and the finishing of the paintings, it is Pieter who deserves the admiration from all those who love Ganga for creating such a beautifully illustrated story of the river that flows not only on Earth but in the minds and souls of the people of India.

It is our hope that the visuals in this book will please the eyes and that the story of Ganga will purify the heart.

Glossary

Aditi: mother of dwarf Brahmachari

Anshuman: King Sagar's last son

Ashram: dwelling place, hermitage

Ashwamedh Yagya: horse sacrifice

Aum Namah Shivaye: the most famous five-syllable mantra to invoke Shiva

Aum Shri Ganeshaye Namah Aum: mantra for Ganesh, the obstacle remover. Ganesh's name is always invoked at the beginning of any act (physical, psychological, or spiritual) to ensure good fortune. The addition of *Aum* at the beginning and ending of the mantra enhances the manta's power by sealing it from both sides.

Bhagirath: seventh generation son of King Sagar, who invoked Lord Brahma to bring the divine river Ganga to Earth to eradicate the sins of his ancestors. The river Ganga became known as the Bhagirathi in his honor.

Bhu Loka: Earth

Boon: gifts of the divine beings

Brahma: creator of the world

Brahma Loka: abode of Lord Brahma, the eighth plane of the Earth plane. See *Leela: The Game of Self-Knowledge* by Harish Johari for a further explanation.

Chakravarti King: Emperor of Earth

Devi: divine female form, goddess

Dharma: code of conduct; the inherent nature of someone or something

Diggaj: elephant (*dig* or *dik* means direction, *gaj* means elephant)

Durvasa: a great sage and rishi, who is famous for getting irritated quickly. Durvasa cursed Ganga and made her become a river on Earth.

Ganga: Devi Ganga. Ganga is the adopted daughter of Lord Brahma. She was born from water in Lord Brahma's kamandalu that washed Lord Vishnu's feet. Ganga later becomes Janhvi, the purified daughter of Rishi Janu, and her river becomes known as Bhagirathi in honor of Bhagirath, whose prayers brought her down to Earth.

Homa: fire sacrifice

Indra: king of heaven and subgods

Janu: the rishi who consumed Ganga and released her, purified, from his thigh

Japa: repetition

Kailash: mountain in Tibet (formerly in India), now occupied by China

Kali Yuga: Age of Darkness. The present era we are in today.

Kamandalu: waterpot

Kapil: the sage who cursed the sons of Sagar and then burned them with his yoga agni

Kashyap: father of dwarf Brahmachari

King Sagar: father of 60,001 sons who tries to expand his kingdom throughout Earth with the Ashwamedh Yagya

Kuber: god in charge of divine treasures

Lakshmi: Vishnu's wife (consort)

Lokas: plane or dwelling place. See *Leela: The Game of Self-Knowledge* by Harish Johari for a more complete explanation of the various lokas and their significance.

Mantra: combination of psychically potent sound syllables in verse form that are used to invoke energy or a deity inherent in the power of the sounds. Also means advice or suggestions. It can be an auto-suggestion, such as "let me be healthy."

Patal Loka: Underworld

Pooja pots: pots used for worship

Rishi: a high being who has complete control over his senses and mind and can see the past, present, and future. Rishi means seer—one who is completely absorbed, has no distractions, can be impartial, and exists on a higher level of consciousness in which all life becomes divine.

Sadhna: period of ritualistic worship. Austerity, discipline.

Sagar: ocean

Samadhi: deepest state of meditation, total absorption

Samkalpa: ritual preceding charitable offerings

Shiva: destroyer of the world. Shiva is the most important of the three gods in the triad (Brahma, Shiva, and Vishnu), because Shiva is the one responsible for change both in the form of death and destruction and in the positive sense of the shedding of old habits.

Shukracharya: King Bali's teacher and advisor and the guru of demons

Surabhi: Vashishtha's wish-fulfilling cow

Swaga Loka: Heaven

Tapas: strictly following a discipline for a particular period of time (can be 100 years, 1000 years) to get at the realization of truth. Austerity, penance.

Varun: lord of waters, ocean

Vashishta: mind-born son of Lord Brahma who cursed the eight vasus for stealing his wish-fulfilling cow

Vasus: guardian angels of eight directions. They stole Vashishtha's cow and need Ganga to drown them in her waters so they can be freed from Vashishtha's curse.

Viman: divine air crafts, carriages that fly in the air

Vishnu: preserver of the world. Comes before King Bali as the dwarf Brahmachari. Vishnu has ten incarnations: fish, turtle, boar, half man/half lion, Vaman (the dwarf), Parshuram Ram, Dalram Ram, Krishna, Buddha, and Kaliki (the future incarnation to end the Kali Yuga).

Yagya: worship of fire or offering to fire

Yoga agni: yoga fire. Comes from the third eye. Yoga agni burned the sons of Sagar.